Decodable Readers 24–32

Scot

Editorial Offices: Glenvi
Sales Offices: Reading, I ..., Georgia
Glenview, Illinois • Carroll. , .cxas • Menlo Park, California

Printed in the United States of America

ISBN 0-673-65179-7

3 4 5 6 7 8 9 10 - BISF - 06 05 04 03 02 01 00

Contents

Jake Is Missing!

by Pamela Michaels
illustrated by Lisa Blackshear

Is something missing? Call
on Jane. Jane will take the
case.

Missing planes? Missing
canes? Missing skates? Jane
will crack the case.

Dave called on Jane to find
his pet snake. Jake is missing!

Jake is not in the tub.

Jake is not in his cage.

Dave gave Jane the case.

Dave called Jake. Dave
yelled his name.

"A snake can not call
back," Jane said.

Jane will get Jake. Jane
can find him.

Jane and Dave looked
by the bed.
Dave called, "Jake, Jake!"

Jane and Dave looked in
the vase and by the gate.
Dave called, "Jake, Jake!"

"It is late," said Dave.
"It is time for bed."
"That is it!" Jane yelled.

"Jake is in bed!"
Jane yelled.

Jake is in bed. Jane
cracked the case!

Phonics Skill Long *a* (CVCe): *Jane, take, case, plane(s), cane(s), skate(s), Dave, snake, Jake, cage, gave, name, vase, gate, late*

Phonics Skill Inflected Ending -ed: *called, yelled, looked, cracked*

Spelling Words: *late, take, gave*

Space Cake

by Nat Gabriel
illustrated by Remy Sinard

Mom makes cake.

Mom calls it space cake.

Blaze helps.

Blaze will mix the cake.

21

A space cake has chips.
Dale adds them.

Chop, chop, chop!

Tap, tap, tap!

A space cake has dates.

23

Blaze fills the cake pans.

Then Mom bakes the cake!

The cake bakes.

Dale and Mom chat.

The cake is hot.

Mom and Dale play a game.

The game is called chess.

Blaze gets the cake on a plate.

It did not sit face up.

Blaze gets mad.

Mom has to fix it.

Dale jumps and jumps.
Blaze races to save the cake.

Blaze saves the space cake.

Mom made it.

Dale and Mom and Blaze
will eat it.

Phonics Skill Long *a* (CVCe): *make(s), cake, space, Blaze, Dale, date(s), bake(s), game, plate, face, race(s), save, made*

Phonics Skill Initial Digraphs *ch, th:* *the, chips, them, chop, then, chat, chess*

Spelling Words: *tap, mad, made*

Dave Bakes Cakes

REVIEW

by Marilyn Fenlon
illustrated by Winson Trang

This is Dave. Dave bakes
cakes. Dave bakes red cakes.
Dave makes pink cakes.

Dave makes lots of cakes.
Dave makes big cakes and
small cakes. Dave makes
cakes with names on them.
Dave makes cakes with faces
on them.

Dave baked a cake for
Jake. Dave baked a cake with
planes for Jake.

Jake ate his cake with
planes.

Dave baked a cake for
Kate. Kate had a cake with
skates.

Kate ate the cake with
skates.

Nate called Dave. Nate missed his cake.

Dave takes a cake to Nate.

Dave gave Nate a small cake on his plate.

Sam was sad. Sam bumped
his chin on his gate.
Dave made a cake for Sam.

Dave made a ball and bat cake. Dave made this cake big.

Dave gave Sam his cake. "This is fun," said Sam.

Phonics Skill Long *a* (CVCe): *Dave, bakes, cakes, makes, names, faces, baked, cake, Jake, planes, ate, Kate, skates, Nate, takes, gave, plate, gate, made*

Phonics Skill Inflected Ending *–ed:* *, called, missed, bumped*

Phonics Skill Initial Digraphs *th* and *ch:* *this, them, the, chin*

Spelling Words: *ate, gave, make, take(s), bake, made*

Whales

by Lorraine McCombs
illustrated by Randy Chewning

Whales can swim.

Whales swim and swim.

Whales are at home in water.

This ship spots whales.

This whale is close.

It waves at us.

This whale is big!

It is as big as a bus.

This whale is little.

This whale can jump.

It jumps up fast!

Not all whales have teeth.

This whale has them.

This whale does not.

This whale has a hole on top.
In water, the hole shuts.

This whale has two holes on top.

In water, those holes close.

The holes close as its top dips in.

Whales jump and hop waves.

This whale jumps up and up.

It is fun.

Whales can do tricks.

This whale did a trick.

It gets a pat on its nose.

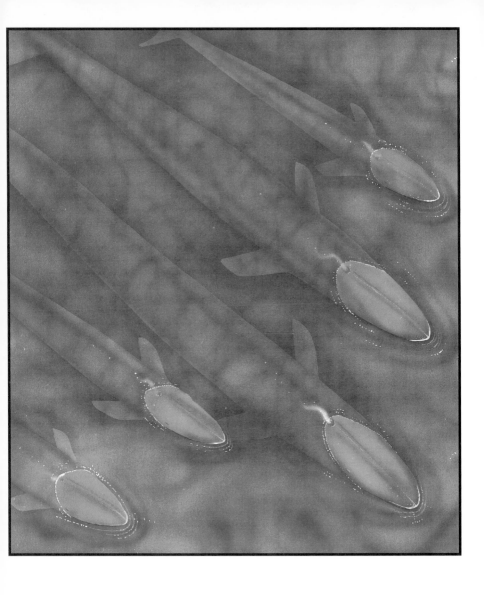

Whales swim well.

Whales are at home in water.

Phonics Skill Long *o* (CVCe): *home, close (adj.), hole, holes, those, close (v.), nose*

Phonics Skill Initial Digraphs *sh*, *wh*: *whales, whale, ship, shuts*

Spelling Words: *home, those*

Pine Lake

by Roger Langer
illustrated by Amy Young

Soon it will be summer.
It is fun. The sun will shine.
It is time to skate and ride
my white bike. That makes
me smile.

It is time! I will see Miles at Pine Lake. We will swim, dive, and hike. Pine Lake will be fun.

This is Pine Lake. It is big and wide. This place is like home. It is nice and quite big. Pine Lake is fun!

Miles is at Pine Lake. Miles is nice. His cat had kittens! Miles likes them all.

Mom, Dad, and I went
on hikes. We went miles
and miles. Dad spotted five
small rabbits. I picked up
nine big pine cones.

We all went fishing. Fishing was fun. Dad and I got five fish. Mom helped us get them.

Dad made a big rock
pile. Mom made a fire in it.
We ate up those five fish.
Yum! Yum!

Miles and I went back in
Pine Lake. Miles dove in.
Then I did. Pine Lake is fun!

Miles and I went on a hike. We went up big hills. This time we got to the top. It was quite nice.

Miles and his mom made snacks. We ate them with jam. Yum! Yum!

It is time to drive home. I am sad. I hope next time at Pine Lake will be just as much fun!

Phonics Skill Long *i* (CVCe): *shine, time, ride, white, bike, smile, Miles, Pine, dive, hike, wide, like, nice, quite, like(s), hike(s), mile(s), five, nine, pine, pile, fire, drive*

Phonics Skill Medial Consonants: *summer, kittens, rabbits*

Spelling Words: *like, nice, time, ride, white, five*

Five White Mice

REVIEW

by Jeff Peters
illustrated by Philip Smith

Five white mice rode
bikes. Five white mice made
jokes when they spoke. The
mice made a stop at a stone.

Five white mice hiked up a hill.

"This spot is nice. Let's stop," five white mice said.

Five white mice rested in the shed's shade.

Five white mice sat on
stones and ate muffins and
rice. The five white mice did
not see the hidden kitten.

The kitten woke.

"This kitten is thin as a bone," said five white mice. "When will it fatten up? Will it fatten up on us?"

"It is time to go. It is not
safe. Let's get home!" yelled
five white mice. Then five
white mice ran to five bikes.

Five white mice left as
quick as a whip. Those white
mice had gotten a shock.

Five white mice rode
bikes. Five white mice did not
stop. Those white mice felt
safe at home.

Phonics Skill Long *o* (CVCe): *rode, jokes, spoke, stone, stones, woke, bone, home, those*

Phonics Skill Initial Digraphs *sh, wh*: *white, when, shed's, shade, whip, shock*

Phonics Skill Long *i* (CVCe): *five, white, mice, bikes, hiked, nice, rice, time*

Phonics Skill Medial Consonants Single and Double: *muffins, hidden, kitten, fatten, gotten*

Spelling Words: *rode, those, hope, home, joke, stone, nice, time, ride, white, five*

Dude Ranch Dudes

by Amy Moses
illustrated by Sharon Vargo

Duke woke up with pink spots.

Duke had spots on his neck.

Duke had spots on his legs.

Duke had spots on his back.

"I itch," said Duke.

"Rub that itch," said Klute.

Duke did rub that itch.

"Stop that," said June.

"It is a bad rash."

Duke did rub that itch.

Duke had lots of spots.

"Rubbing that itch is funny,"
said Klute.
"This rash is not funny,"
said Duke.

"How will I play?" Duke asked.

"All I can do is rub this itch."

"How will I sing?" Duke asked.
Duke wished his spots didn't
itch.

The
Dude Ranch Dudes
Band

Duke, June, and Klute left.
All went to the Dude Ranch.

Those Dude Ranch Dudes
sang!
Duke had to rub an itch.
Duke had to rub and rub!

The mules stopped to watch.

Duke had to rub and rub.

Duke didn't stop singing.

Then those mules all did it!

They did it just like Duke.

It was such fun!

Phonics Skill Long *u* (CVCe): *Dude, Dudes, Duke, Klute, June, mules*

Phonics Skill Final Digraphs *ch, tch, sh, th, ng, nk:* *with, pink, itch, rash, sing, wish(ed), Ranch, sang, watch, singing, such*

Spelling Words: *the, that, with, such*

Seeds

by P. Linda Lynk
illustrated by Jane Chambless Wright

I saw that man. He came
up a hill. His steps were big.
He had long legs.

He had a pot for his hat.
He had a pack on his back.
He ate a snack.

Who is he?

He cannot see me yet.

Let me run up this hill.

I ran to meet that man.
I ran fast and tapped his
backpack.

Let me see that hat.
Is that pot hot?
Let me see that pack.
It is big. What is in it?

I peeked inside his pack.
It was filled with seeds.

The man gave me lots
of seeds.
He liked planting seeds.

Seeds need to be planted.
The man helped me plant
them.

We dug a deep hole.

Seeds need sunshine.

Seeds need water.

See those seeds now!

Those seeds are green trees!

Phonics Skill Long e spelled ee, e: *he, see, me, meet, peek, peeked, seeds, need, be, we, deep, green, trees*

Phonics Skill Compound Words: *cannot, backpack, inside, sunshine*

Spelling Words: *we, me, he, see, green*

Luke and June See Granddad

REVIEW

by Donna Baker
illustrated by Kate Flanagan

We ride in the jeep. We
get to see Granddad.

"See that?" Dad asks.

"Yes, I can see six mules,"
calls Luke.

"Are we at Granddad's
yet?" June asks.

"This is a long, long ride!"
Luke yells.

We ride in the jeep. We get to see Granddad.

"See that?" Dad asks.

"Yes, I can see ten bees and a beehive," June tells him.

"Are we at Granddad's
yet?" asks Luke.

"This is a long, long ride!"
yells June.

"See that?" ask June and
Luke.

"I cannot see it," Dad calls.

"Look, in back of that green
plant," June tells him.

"See that huge bobcat? I wish Granddad was with us to see it," calls Luke. "Let's get Granddad."

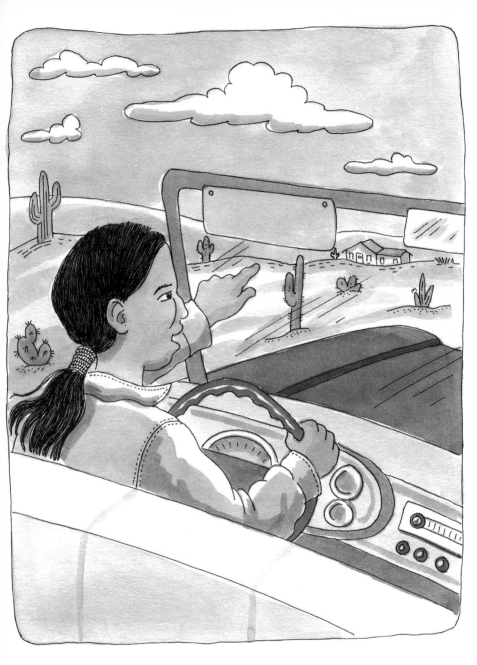

"See that?" Dad asks.

"Granddad!" yell June and Luke.

"Granddad, that bobcat is huge!" Luke yells.

"It is in back of a plant!" June yells.

"This is a long, long ride," calls Dad.

Phonics Skill Long *u* (CVCe): *mules, Luke, June, huge*

Phonics Skill Final Digraphs *th, sh, ng:* *long, wish, with*

Phonics Skill Long *e* Spelled *ee, e:* *we, jeep, see, bees, green*

Phonics Skill Compound Words: *Granddad, beehive, cannot, bobcat*

Spelling Words: *the, that, with, long, we, see, green*